NORMAN BRIDWELL

Clifford's
WORD BOOK

BARN

HORSE

COW

FARMER

PIG

SCHOLASTIC INC.

New York Toronto London Auckland Sydney

Dedicated to Nadia Miret.
— N.B.

ISBN 0-590-43094-7

Copyright © 1990 by Norman Bridwell.
All rights reserved. Published by Scholastic Inc.

CLIFFORD and CLIFFORD THE BIG RED DOG are registered trademarks of Scholastic Inc.

12 11 10 9 8 7 6 5 4 3 2 1   0 1 2 3 4 5/9

Printed in the U.S.A.   23

First Scholastic printing, January 1990

sky

tree

house

dog

grass

girl

My name is Emily Elizabeth
and this is my big red dog, Clifford.

picture

plant

hook

bed

clock

dresser

book

pillow

blanket

slippers

rug

hanger

radio

Clifford is too big to fit inside my room.
But he can still keep me company.

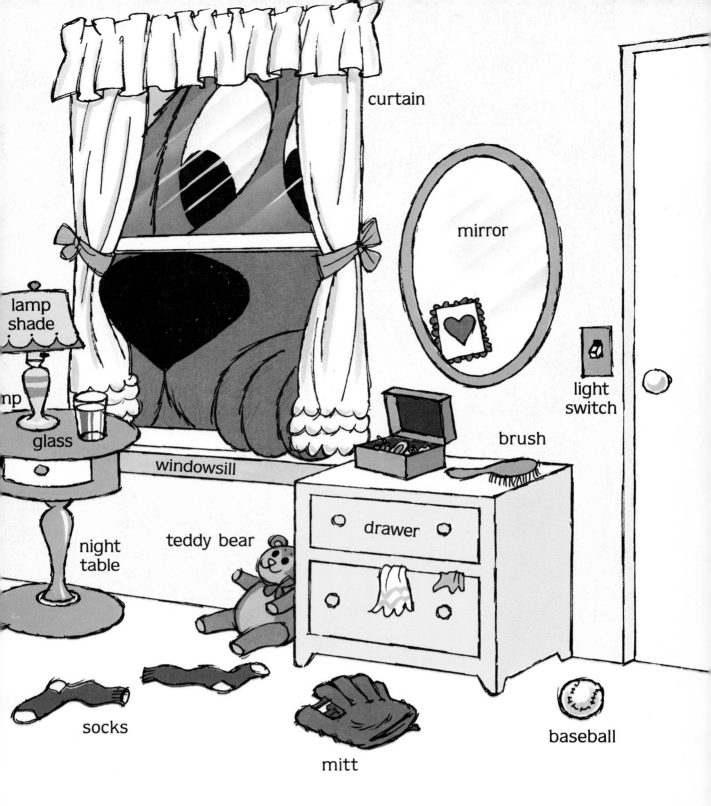

curtain

mirror

lamp
shade

light
switch

np

brush

glass

windowsill

night
table

teddy bear

drawer

socks

baseball

mitt

kite

football

glider

jump rope

yo-yo

rocking horse

wagon

train

toy car

Like all dogs, Clifford has a favorite toy.
What's your favorite toy?

soccer ball

bat

stuffed monkey

dinosaur

crayons

tennis racket

puzzle

dollhouse

carriage

baseball

tea set

rattle

blocks

top

jacks

doll

flag

streetlight

BARBER SHOP

barber pole

49

bananas

watermelons
pineapples

bench

fire
hydrant

And he likes to go for walks.
This is the main street of our town.

Everybody knows Clifford.
And everybody likes Clifford.

photographer

magician

baseball player

queen

king

farmer

jester

fire fighter

to mechanic

musician

jockey

fisherman

alphabet

clock

hat

chalkboard

$3 \times 3 = 9$

map

$\begin{array}{r} 2 \\ +4 \\ \hline 6 \end{array}$

bookcase

pen

chalkboard eraser

chalk

globe

book

scissors

wasteba

desk

boots

jacke

Clifford waits for me while I'm in school.
I can see him outside the window.

train

truck

unicycle

tugboat

car

jet

jeep

helicopter

hot-air
balloon

race car

sailboat

submarine

motorcycle

canoe

Clifford likes things that move.
I tell him not to chase cars.
But sometimes he forgets.

In the afternoon, we play in the park.
Clifford is even more fun than a swing!

swings

jungle gym

fountain

picnic table

slide

sandbox

seesaw

guitar

trumpet

xylophone

tambourine

bow

violin

triangle

piano

saxophone

Clifford loves listening to music.
He is a good singer.

maracas

accordion

note

bell

French horn

sheet music

singer

conductor

bassoon

tuba

harp

trombone

drum

cymbals

apple trees

field

scarecr

sheep

sunflowers

clothes line

water pump

basket

farmhouse

birdbath

wheelbarro

porch

chickens

Clifford's sister lives on a farm in the country.
Clifford visits her often.

igloo

beehive

grass hut

nest

tepee

camper

dog house

CLIFFORD

castle

Clifford's home is a dog house.
We built it just for him.

tent

house

burrow

adobe house

apartment building

log cabin

cave

trapeze

hoop

pie

ringmaster

tiger

juggler

dogs

Once the circus came to town.
Clifford helped to put on a show.

sea lion

turtle

camel

kangaroo

elephant

Clifford is so big.
He's even bigger than an elephant!

rhinoceros

penguin

octopus

gorilla

panda

deer

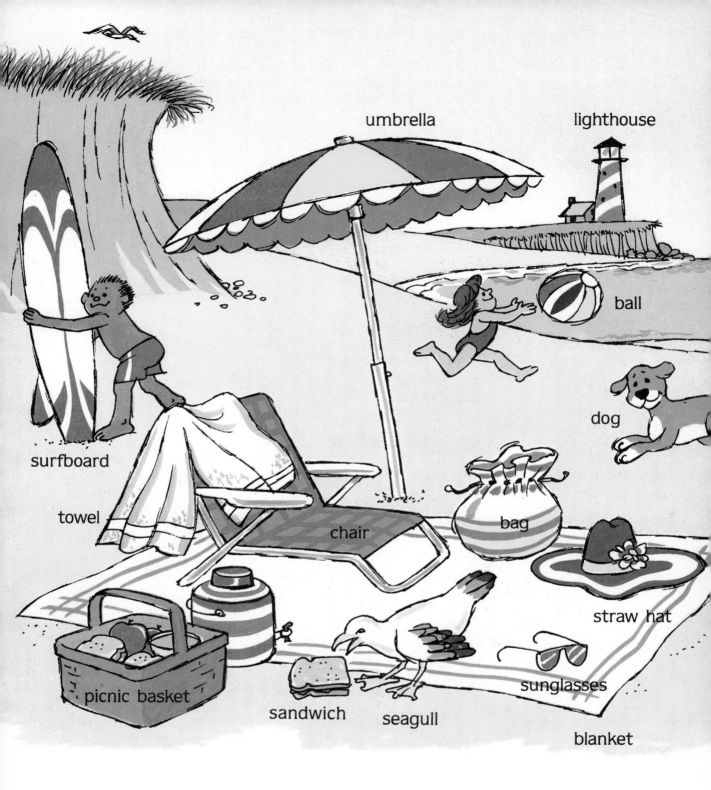

umbrella

lighthouse

ball

dog

surfboard

towel

chair

bag

straw hat

sunglasses

picnic basket

sandwich

seagull

blanket

sun

seaplane

raft

ocean

lobster

sandpipers

seaweed

horseshoe crab

shovel

sand castle

starfish

sand

In the summer we go to the beach.
Clifford does the dog paddle.

WHITE

snowman

dove

shirt

BLACK

ants

bat

bow tie

RED

Clifford

apple

heart

ORANGE

pumpkin

carrots

oranges

YELLOW

lemon

daffodil

cheese

My favorite color is red.
Clifford likes that color, too!

GREEN

leaf

beans

grasshopper

BLUE

blueberries

ribbon

cap

PURPLE

violets

plums

crocuses

GRAY

mouse

stone

slacks

PINK

cupcake

rose

strawberry ice cream

BROWN

acorns

pinecone

paper bag

On Clifford's birthday his family and friends celebrate.
We love you, Clifford!